Exploring The Columbia Icefield

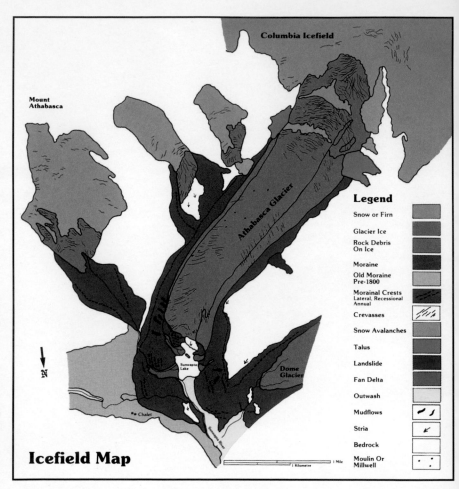

Icefield Map

Legend

Snow or Firn

Glacier Ice

Rock Debris On Ice

Moraine

Old Moraine Pre-1800

Morainal Crests
Lateral, Recessional Annual

Crevasses

Snow Avalanches

Talus

Landslide

Fan Delta

Outwash

Mudflows

Stria

Bedrock

Moulin Or Millwell

Exploring The Columbia Icefield

by Richard E. Kucera, Ph.D.

Published by  HIGH COUNTRY COLOUR

2

CONTENTS

INTRODUCTION 5
DISCOVERY AND BRIEF HISTORY 6
COLUMBIA ICEFIELD AND GLACIERS 10
ATHABASCA GLACIER 12
HOW IS A GLACIER FORMED? 14
OPPOSING FORCES ON THE GLACIER. 18
A CLOSE LOOK AT THE ICE 19
    Ice Crystals and Foliation of the Ice
    Why is the Ice Blue?
FLOW OF THE ICE 21
    Internal Deformation
    Basal Sliding
    Crevasses
    Icequakes
HOW FAST DOES THE GLACIER MOVE? 26
HOW THICK IS THE ICE? 28
FLUCTUATIONS OF THE ICE FRONT 29
    Evidence of Glacier Advance
    A Glacier in Retreat
    The Disappearing Glacier
HOW DOES THE GLACIER ERODE BEDROCK? 34
GLACIAL SCULPTURE 35
GLACIAL DEPOSITION 36
    Lateral Moraines
    Ablation Moraines
    Ground Moraines
    Annual Moraines
    Recessional Moraines
GLACIAL MELTWATER 45
Meltwater Channels and Moulins
SUNWAPTA LAKE AND DELTAS 48
THE SUNWAPTA FLOODS. 49
GLACIAL OUTWASH 51
RECENT OBSERVATIONS 54
    Glacial Transport
    Moderating Effects of Snow
MOUNTAIN SLOPES THAT MOVE 55
    Cause of Accelerated Slope Movements
AVALANCHE ACTIVITY 60
A GLIMPSE INTO THE PAST 61
A LOOK INTO THE FUTURE 62
ACKNOWLEDGEMENTS 65
SELECTED REFERENCES. 66
GLOSSARY 68

Aerial view of the Columbia Icefield. The Athabasca Glacier and Dome Glacier descend from the ice-covered upland. Photograph by John S. Shelton (1964).

INTRODUCTION

Everyone fortunate enough to return over the years to the Athabasca Glacier poses questions about its future, and about its complex glacial past. At the turning point of a new century, what degree of change will impact its magnificent features?

Events in the life of this reknowned, accessible glacier and the massive icefield and peaks above it are the focus of the new edition of *Exploring the Columbia Icefield.* This fifth and revised edition of the book highlights mountain exploration and photography by the author, documenting more than two decades of research in this spectacular region. The story of the glaciers, and the Columbia Icefield continues on these pages with new chapters and forty-four new photographs which show the evolution of the landscape at the front, or toe of the glacier. If you explore the area, you may discover that the sharp crests of the lateral moraines, the precipitous cliffs, and rough mountain slopes are subjected in time to a long, awesome attack by powerful geological forces. Overcoming these adverse conditions, the beauty of the Columbia Icefield is undiminished.

Approaching the Columbia Icefield from the north along the Icefield Parkway.

DISCOVERY AND BRIEF HISTORY

Athabasca Glacier descends from the Columbia Icefield in spectacular icefalls.

The Canadian Pacific Railroad was completed in 1885, and from that time onward, Banff and Lake Louise became widely known as resort destinations. In contrast, to the north in the wilder mountain country which would later be designated as Jasper National Park, one of the most massive glacial features in the Canadian Rockies lay beyond discovery for more than another decade. A history-making event took place when a group of experienced climbers sent by the Royal Geographical Society came to solve the mystery regarding the height of the famous peaks, Mt. Hooker and Mt. Brown. With luck, the climbers scaled a different peak, reaching the vantage point where they discovered the Columbia Icefield.

Before dawn on August 18, 1898, two men in the climbing party, Hermann Woolley and J. Norman Collie, left their camp and began the ascent of this peak, which they named Mt. Athabasca. At 3491 metres, on the snow-clad summit, the two alpine climbers were left in awe of the magnificent scene around them. Reflecting on the new realm of ice which they had encountered and named, the expedition leader, Scotsman Norman Collie later recalled:

"The view that lay before us in the evening light was one that does not often fall to the lot of modern mountaineers. A new world was spread at our feet: to the westward stretched a vast icefield probably never before seen by human eye, and surrounded by entirely unknown, unnamed, and unclimbed peaks. From its vast expanse of snows the Saskatchewan Glacier takes its rise, and it also supplies the headwaters of the Athabasca; while far away to the west, bending over in those unknown valleys glowing with the evening light, the level snows stretched, to finally melt and flow down more than one channel to the Columbia River, and thence to the Pacific Ocean."

The undaunted mountaineers, including Hugh Stutfield, made another ascent to the source of the Athabasca Glacier. In 1898, the glacier was not as advanced as it had been in 1840. However, it was still more than 7 km long, and its terminus was a thick mass of ice which touched the far side of Sunwapta Valley. The glacier blocked passage from Banff to Jasper, except by the route of the higher pass discovered by American mountaineer Walter Wilcox, two years before. After he reached the edge of the Columbia Icefield, Norman Collie's thoughts were eloquent:

"We stood on the edge of an immense icefield, bigger than the biggest in Switzerland, that is to say, than the Ewige Sneefeld and the Aletsch Glacier combined — which stretched mile upon mile before us like a rolling snow covered prairie. The peaks, we noticed, were all a long way off, and sparser and fewer in number than in the Alps, rising only here and there like rocky islets from a frozen sea."

Guides on horseback at terminus of Athabasca Glacier (1914). Courtesy of Peter and Catharine Whyte Foundation (Archives of the Canadian Rockies).

In the years following the discovery of the Columbia Icefield, Swiss guides, as well as mountaineers and writers, and Alberta pioneers such as Tom Wilson, Jimmy Simpson, Bill Peyto, and Jim Brewster, were engaged in breaking trails to the lakes, glaciers, and peaks. Professor A.P. Coleman of Toronto was the great geologist of the era. Journals of the time attracted many enthusiastic adventurers from distant points in North America and Europe in the ensuing years.

Photographs taken by courageous explorer, Mary Schäffer, captured timeless images of the Columbia Icefield, the Athabasca Glacier, exquisite alpine meadows, Maligne Lake, and other scenes of the backcountry. Some of the finest views taken by photographers portrayed a rugged life in isolated camps. Horses were used by guiding parties to ford the rivers such as the North Saskatchewan, and great hazards were overcome as they traversed new routes to the Columbia Icefield.

THE ATHABASCA GLACIER AND SURROUNDING PEAKS.

In later years, views from Wilcox Pass showed the red roofs and interesting character of the Columbia Icefield Chalet, which served for decades as a starting point of great adventure for generations of hikers. In the year 2000, mountain climbers, geologists, artists and photographers will have covered more than a century of exploring and describing the Athabasca Glacier, nearby alpine valleys, and the Columbia Icefield. Paintings of the landscape, many created by Alberta artists, enhanced the play of light and shadow on the great expanse of the ice and snow beneath the high peaks. The Columbia Icefield, in the past, present and future, is the heart of a challenging region for mountain climbers. Famous routes for mountaineers include the ascents of Snow Dome, Stutfield Peak, Mt. Kitchener, Mount Columbia, and many other peaks.

From left: Mt. Athabasca, Mt. Andromeda, Athabasca Glacier, Dome Glacier.

COLUMBIA ICEFIELD AND GLACIERS

Among the most impressive peaks of the Canadian Rocky Mountains, the distinctive, rounded Snow Dome is unique. Rising above the surrounding expanse of the Columbia Icefield, this easily recognized peak, at an elevation of 3456 metres, is of interest to scientists, for its mantle of snow and glacial ice is the source of meltwater which begins a journey down its slopes, and then eventually flows into the rivers which reach three oceans, the Atlantic, Pacific, and the Arctic.

There are a number of beautiful and extensive icefields in the Rockies, such as the Freshfield, Lyell, Wapta, and the Clemenceau, as well as others which survive at high altitudes. The massive Columbia Icefield is in a class by itself, consisting of deep glacial ice which blankets an area of approximately 325 square kilometres. Estimated to be more than 200 metres thick in certain areas within its boundaries, it closely approximates the topography and character of the immense icefields which existed in Canada during the great Ice Ages. Year by year, it is slowly decreasing in area and volume of ice. Because the icefield is protected by formidable peaks, including eleven of the highest summits of the Canadian Rocky Mountains, an unobstructed sight of the icefield is quite elusive from the valleys below.

Aerial view of the Columbia Icefield. Beneath the rim, tongues of ice spill out from the icefield and flow into surrounding valleys.

Best seen from the air, or explored on skis during a cross-country expedition, the Columbia Icefield is noted for its huge irregular shape, for the precipitous ice cliffs on its perimeter, and for its vast, gently rolling surfaces of ice and snow which stretch across a lofty plateau along the spine of the mountains. This superb icefield, which is still more than 100 metres thick at its outer rim, spans the Continental Divide, along the border between Alberta and British Columbia. It exists in magnificent isolation, at a high elevation in both Banff and Jasper National Parks.

First impressions of an immense, stable mass of ice are deceptive, for the Columbia Icefield is accumulating layers of fresh snow, which are being transformed into ice throughout its primary accumulation area. There is dramatic activity along its abrupt outer rim, for the icefield spills an almost continual flow of ice down into a ring of valley outlet glaciers, which depend upon the replenishment for their existence. Counted among the best known valley outlet glaciers are the Saskatchewan, the Columbia, and the Dome, Stutfield, and Athabasca Glaciers.

One of these major tributary ice tongues is the Columbia Glacier, which ultimately feeds the extensive Athabasca River drainage system. Some of most spectacular valley glaciers have been studied by geologists for more than half a century. The largest glacier in the region is the Saskatchewan, the source of the North Saskatchewan River. An impressive tongue of glacial ice, less complex, but occupying a greater area than the Athabasca Glacier, the Saskatchewan can be seen on a hike to the Parker Ridge viewpoint, or on a long passage through its valley to study its geological features.

The Saskatchewan Glacier is rich in human history, including the early horseback expeditions led by some of the famous mountain guides. It is also remembered as the site of Canadian and American alpine military maneuvers, in preparation for WWII in Europe. Canadian mountaineering troops were billeted at the Columbia Icefield Chalet. They were expert climbers of the surrounding peaks.

It is fortunate that high altitude, a cold micro-climate, deep snowfall, protective peaks, and the great expanse of the glacial ice will assure that the Columbia Icefield will be able to resist some of the ravages of current global warming.

ATHABASCA GLACIER

The Athabasca Glacier flows through its steep-sided alpine valley for a distance of 5.5 km, measured from the elevation where it descends from the Columbia Icefield at approximately 2700 metres. Each year, the critical distance covered by the glacier will change, for as the ice advances, it also experiences a greater rate of recession at its terminus.

Flowing from the icefield, the glacier cascades downward in a series of three steep, chaotic, and crevassed icefalls which descend over hidden bedrock cliffs. The glacier then continues at a more gentle gradient as a tongue of ice about 0.7 km wide, for a distance of 3.5 km down its valley. Considered to be the most classically-featured glacier in the Canadian Rockies, the Athabasca Glacier reaches its terminus at an elevation of about 2000 metres, where it is extremely accessible for glaciological research and exploration.

The slope of the glacier surface just below the lowest icefall ranges from 3° to 7°. The deep and extensive central section of the glacier is in this area, where the ice is very thick and relatively less crevassed. This broad glacial surface provides a unique access area for visitors on the ice, crossing the glacier on the custom designed Brewster Snocoaches.

The toe of the glacier had a slope of 15° in 1995. This icy, heavily crevassed surface has a markedly different configuration from year to year,

Retreat of the Athabasca Glacier reveals a high bedrock ridge on the right.
A meltwater stream enters Sunwapta Lake.

as the glacial ice experiences a dramatic loss of volume. This loss of ice is the greatest threat to the future of the glacier.

A great contribution of the Athabasca Glacier to the ecology of the region is the release of powerful meltwater streams from portals at the terminus of the glacier. The huge volume of meltwater flows into Sunwapta Lake, then into the Sunwapta River, joins the Athabasca, and then continues a great distance to the Mackenzie River, finally entering the Arctic Ocean. Glacial meltwater is indeed the source of life for a vast territory.

The Athabasca Glacier has appealing features, yet it is known that its crevasses and moulins are dangerous to hikers who venture on treacherous ice without prior climbing experience, good equipment, or an alpine guide. Parks Canada interpretive staff at the Icefield Centre are a good source of information concerning ice conditions. They have detailed knowledge of the region, and provide excellent advice on mountaineering.

The Athabasca Glacier, and the panorama of impressive peaks which includes the snow-clad summits of Mt. Athabasca and Mt. Andromeda, as well as the icy ramparts on the edge of the Columbia Icefield, may now be seen from a memorable setting, the viewing deck of the new Icefield Centre, which opened in 1996. The Glacier Gallery, with its educational and fun exhibits, is a masterpiece of design to be seen within the centre.

Iceberg in Sunwapta Lake (1964) when the glacier bordered the lake.

HOW IS A GLACIER FORMED?

Late in the summer, it is possible to observe a snowline (the lower limit of perennial snow) which crosses the entire width of the Athabasca Glacier, about half-way down the highest icefall at 2600 metres. Above the snowline (which may be irregular) there are snowfields which endure through the summer, and persist from year to year. Eventually, conditions will be right for a glacier to form.

The transformation of snow into ice depends on winter conditions, with precipitation in the form of snow, and there must be ample time for the process to work. To begin the formation of a glacier, the yearly accumulation of new snow must be greater than the amount of snow lost both to melting and to evaporation.

Low temperature alone cannot assure the growth of the snowfield. It is where the winter snowpack is so deep that summer melting and evaporation fail to remove it all, that snowfields are formed and maintained. It is estimated that approximately 10 metres of snow falls in the Columbia Icefield region each year. From season to season, throughout the years, a healthy snowfield increases its depth.

As the loose, feathery snow is buried by successive falls, it is gradually transformed into firn, or closely packed spherical granules of old snow, measuring less than 3 mm in diameter, with inter-connected air spaces. In time, the whole mass takes on more of a granular texture, similar to what we find in snowdrifts at winter's end. With further compaction, more air is squeezed out, meltwater seeps in, freezes, and recrystalizes until the deeper layers of firn are eventually transformed into ice.

Over a period of years these accumulations become deeper, and compressed enough to form glacier ice. When a critical thickness is reached, the ice begins to move and flow down the valley, influenced by the pull of gravity, following the path of least resistance.

Climbing the steep front of the Athabasca Glacier.

Photomicrograph of typical crystalline mosaic of glacier ice. Each small area of color is a single crystal as seen in polarized light. The tiny circular spots are bubbles of air. Actual size 3 cm wide. From A. J. Gow, U.S. Army Cold Regions Research and Engineering Laboratory.

A campsite high in the Columbia Icefield (photograph by Brock Carlton).

Glacier of Mt. Athabasca.

Cave of blue ice at terminus of Athabasca Glacier. (now collapsed)

Perfect ice crystals shimmer in tunnel beneath the Athabasca Glacier.

OPPOSING FORCES ON THE GLACIER

The glacier may not have the appearance of a battleground, but there is a constant war of opposing natural forces which will determine the existence and long-term future of the Athabasca Glacier. This is a situation in which the two major zones of the glacier must compete for area. The upper area of the glacier, at higher elevations and colder temperatures, where more snow can accumulate instead of melting, is called the *zone of accumulation.*

The lower part of the glacier, which is subjected to higher air temperatures, is known as the *zone of ablation,* for more ice is lost there by melting and evaporation. In winter, it is difficult to see a line between the zones, because a fresh blanket of snow disguises much of the glacial surface, even concealing a number of crevasses. In the summer, it is most striking to see the perennial snow surface of the upper Athabasca Glacier, for it looks pristine in contrast to the ablation zone, which reveals patchy snow, bare ice, ablation debris, large rocks, fine dust, and unusual features such as the dirt cones. Artifacts from previous years are found in the dirt cones, for these odd features on the ice began as small depressions where debris formerly accumulated. Visitors to the lower part of the glacier are often surprised to discover that the "messy" covering of rock fragments on the ice surface is a natural phenomenon, taking place on most alpine glaciers throughout other mountain ranges of the world.

The state of health of the glacier is estimated by determining the *glacier budget.* Over a period of time, when the amount of snow and ice gained by the glacier is greater than the amount of ice and water it loses, then the glacier's budget is *positive,* and in time the glacier will expand. If the opposite conditions prevail, then the glacier decreases in volume, and it is said to have a *negative* budget.

Snocoach turnaround, with a view of Mount Andromeda and its glacier.

A CLOSE LOOK AT THE ICE

Ice Crystals and Foliation of the Ice

Below the icefalls, the Athabasca Glacier has layers of white bubbly ice which alternate with fine bluish ice layers. Bordering the Snocoach road, layers of the different ice crystals exist in structures which are inclined steeply toward the west, and extend the length of the glacier. This *foliation* results from plastic deformation of the original ice layers which formed after the initial snowfall accumulated both on the Columbia Icefield, and on the upper Athabasca Glacier.

Darker layers on the glacier surface also result from trapping dust in certain areas. Complex folds of ice reflect the process of plastic flow and deformation of ice deep within the glacier. These features can be seen because ablation (melting and evaporation) of the Athabasca Glacier has allowed us to view the once hidden deeper ice.

Why is the Ice Blue?

Why does the ice vary from shades of white into an intense blue in the Athabasca Glacier? Change in the colour we perceive results from air bubble content, and from the amount of fine debris on the surface and within the ice. Air bubbles prevent penetration of visible light to the deep layers. Most of the light rays are reflected back from the layer closer to the surface, making the surface layer appear white.

When there is comparatively little air in the upper layers of the glacier, the light penetrates to the deeper layers, and the longer visible wavelengths (yellow, orange and red) are readily absorbed. The only rays that remain to be reflected and scattered by air bubbles and rock particles are those of the shorter visible wavelength, so that mostly green and blue reach the eye (Baranowski and Henoch, 1978). The most intense shade of blue ice is seen in the ice caves, moulins, and crevasses. This is the spectacular colour which people want to see when they cross the Athabasca Glacier.

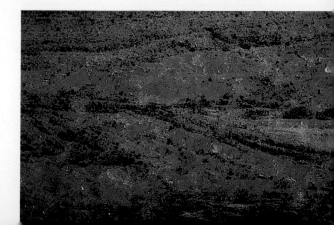

Foliation composed of bluish and white bubbly ice reveals deformation of ice crystals.

Ice is the most intense blue in caves at the toe of the Athabasca Glacier. Huge blocks of ice frequently break off the ceiling, crashing to the bedrock floor. The caves have now collapsed.

FLOW OF THE ICE

Internal Deformation

Glacial ice behaves like a brittle substance until the thickness of the upper layer of the glacier exceeds about thirty-five to fifty metres. Once that depth is surpassed, weight and pressure are sufficient to cause the deeper ice within the glacier to behave like a plastic. Then, glacial flow can begin, responding to the force of gravity.

Stresses at depth cause the ice to change in shape, facilitating down-slope movement. Internal deformation within deeper levels of the glacier is also responsible for the arcuate folds of glacial ice revealed in ice caves and crevasses. (This ice was once at great depth).

In the film *"Glacier on the Move"*, which was made on the Athabasca Glacier, we conducted an experiment at a university laboratory, subjecting the glacial ice to extreme high pressure and duplicating conditions in nature. The experiment, shown on film, demonstrated that the ice became deformed under pressure, and it was then very easy to extrude out of a narrow opening in a metal container. We discovered that the ice yielded to pressure most readily when the temperature of the ice was close to 0° C. (temperature of the greater part of the glacier). The Athabasca Glacier, with ice at or close to the melting point, shows the effect of internal deformation with classic foliation and fold patterns common to *warm glaciers* in many mountain valleys.

Tributary glacier on Mt. Andromeda displays an internal structure of beautiful folds.

Basal Sliding

The second component of glacier flow is basal sliding, whereby the glacier, with the addition of meltwater, slips over its bed. Since the Athabasca Glacier is a warm glacier (close to 0° C) basal sliding may be as high as seventy percent of the total glacial movement. My time-lapse films have documented the action of basal sliding near the terminus of the glacier. You can see the ice moving and dragging boulders along.

Crevasses

As it moves down its valley, the Athabasca Glacier has an outer crust which is brittle, constantly being pulled apart, and then cracking. When the glacial ice is stretched over cliffs, it breaks into steep-sided openings. These fractures in the ice are *crevasses* which are a good indication that the upper layer of the glacier cannot acheive plastic flow.

To the casual observer, the glacier surface is a confusing array of both smaller and larger crevasses, which intersect layers of ice. In the 1970's 30,000 crevasses were counted with the use of aerial photography.

Geologists using seismic data have concluded that the transverse crevasses encountered in the three icefalls in the upper part of the glacier reflect the hidden bedrock steps. The ice descends some 120 meters in the highest icefall and approximately 90 and 70 metres in the other two icefalls. Spectacular crevasses in the lower two icefalls extend almost across the entire width of the glacier. The flow of ice is fastest over the bedrock steps, but at the foot of the icefalls the velocity slows down, and the flow closes the fractures.

Crevasses in upper part of Athabasca Glacier. (air photo)
Inset: measuring depth of a crevasse in the lower icefall.

Marginal crevasses are prominent on both sides of the Snocoach road along the edge of the glacier. They intersect the margin of the glacier at about 45° and extend up-glacier. Individual crevasses can be traced across the ice for over 500 metres, from the bare ice surface into the rubble covered ice, and nearly to the talus slopes flanking the steep bedrock valley walls. These crevasses result from the stresses caused by friction as the glacier moves past the valley walls.

Most marginal crevasses are nearly vertical. Detailed measurements confirm that differential movement of the ice masses takes place on both sides of these fractures. The ice immediately down-glacier from a crevasse can be displaced downward as much as 100 cm in a 72 hour period. Repeated movement along some of these crevasses has caused uneven road conditions which are graded to smooth the way for Snocoach travel.

The crevasses in the Athabasca Glacier extend no deeper than about 36 metres, because greater plastic flow of ice at depth keeps them closed. During a research field trip, we measured 15 of the largest crevasses on the Athabasca Glacier, and the deepest one found on the lower step measured 32 metres in depth.

Hundreds of splaying crevasses extend from the highest icefall for a distance of 0.7 km down-glacier. They fan out due to expansion of the mass of ice as it emerges from the central region of the upper icefall. Splaying crevasses again become pronounced near the terminus of the glacier. These appear to be the result of a slight widening of the valley. As melting occurs, these crevasses open and facilitate the disintegration of ice, particularly at the toe of the glacier, which has become significantly thinner over the last two decades. This is one of the major factors in the rapidly evolving configuration of the glacier front. A covering of fresh snow on the glacier can mask crevasses openings, concealing the danger.

Icequakes

Is it possible that the propagation of crevasses in the glacier is somewhat analogous to faulting and earthquakes in the Earth's crust?

In an interesting geophysical project, researchers Neave and Savage (1970) set up a seismic recording unit on the Athabasca Glacier located about 1.5 km down-glacier from the lowest icefall. A study of the location of epicentres reveals that icequakes generally occur in the marginal crevasse zones. Swarms of icequakes were detected with typical densities of 2 to 10 events per second, and a duration of from 1 to 15 seconds. The individual quakes were distributed along a straight line several hundred metres long. The activity progressed from one end of the line to the other at a speed of about 30 metres per second, behaving like small earthquakes.

Crevasse in Athabasca Glacier (Photo by Hans Fuhrer).

Transverse crevasses in lower icefall of Athabasca Glacier.

Athabasca Glacier descends from Columbia Icefield in three icefalls. Mt. Andromeda and tributary glacier on left.

HOW FAST DOES THE GLACIER MOVE?

The Water Resources Branch of the Department of Northern Affairs and Natural Resources began surveys of certain glaciers on the eastern slope of the Rocky Mountains in 1945. In 1962, metal markers were placed in two lines across the Athabasca Glacier. One line was approximately 300 metres, and the other 1.4 km from the terminus, positioned at right angles to the direction of ice flow. After two years of measuring the position of the markers, the advance of the glacier was calculated.

The differential movement of markers on the glacier revealed that it was moving faster in the middle zone than along its margin. This middle or central zone is much thicker, and the weight of the ice pushing down the valley is much greater, thus causing more rapid flow. Movement at the glacier margin is restricted by friction as the ice is dragged along the bedrock of the valley sides.

Savage and Paterson (1963) measured the surface velocity of the ice at many places on the glacier, showing that along the centre line of flow, the velocity decreases from about 75 metres per year just below the lowest icefall to less than 15 metres per year near the terminus. At such velocities, ice requires decades to travel the length of the glacier. If you sample the ice at the toe of the glacier, remember that 150-200 years have elapsed since the ice long ago fell as snow in the Columbia Icefield!

Time-lapse cinematography and still photography reveal secrets of the Athabasca Glacier. Photographs taken over a three year period show that the ice within 60 metres of the terminus moves at an average rate of 5.7 cm per day (20.8 m/year). Short-term measurements over a 12-hour period in the summer indicate that ice at the toe of the glacier moves as much as 0.25 cm/hour. Photographs taken over a 2 1/2 month period show that the surface ice descends the lowest icefall at a velocity of approximately 127 m/year.

The 16mm time-lapse camera can record processes active at the front of the glacier (see Glacier on the Move, 1973).

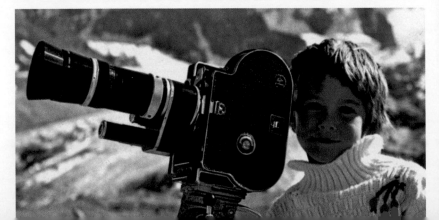

The glacier moves faster during the summer than in the winter, and moves faster during the day than at night. It is thought that changes in velocity result from variations in the amount of water available at the base of the glacier for lubrication. When melting increases in April, May, and through the summer, some surface meltwater will move to the base of the glacier through cracks and channelways. Water reduces friction at the base of the glacier, thus enabling the glacier to speed up. In winter, when there is little meltwater, the velocity slows again, as you would expect.

Drilling through the glacier down to bedrock using electrically powered hot points, geophysicists made important findings. Savage and Paterson, and Raymond, (from 1963 to 1971) proved that the upper part of the glacier moves faster than the base of the glacier.

The following figure shows a typical curve of velocity related to depth. This borehole near the centre line in the ablation area reached bedrock at 209 metres depth. Velocity varies little with depth in the upper half of the borehole; but in the lower half, velocity decreases as the base is approached. The glacier is sliding past bedrock at this location at only 10% of the surface velocity. Elsewhere, basal flow may be as much as 70% of surface velocity of the Athabasca Glacier.

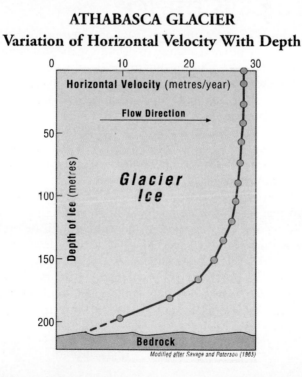

ATHABASCA GLACIER
Variation of Horizontal Velocity With Depth

Modified after Savage and Paterson (1963)

Ice at the toe of the Athabasca Glacier is moving 0.15 to 0.25 cm per hour.

HOW THICK IS THE ICE?

In the summer of 1959, the University of Alberta and the University of British Columbia initiated a study to determine the mechanism of flow of the Athabasca Glacier. During this study, the thickness of the ice and the depth to bedrock were determined by gravity surveys, by hot point drilling, and by seismic methods. Since then, many research groups have participated in related studies.

According to Kanasewich (1963) the ice within the accumulation zone (above the highest icefall) was approximately 220 metres thick, but below the highest icefall it was only 92 metres thick. After descending the second icefall, it thickened again to 195 metres.

For 2 km down the glacier from the lowest icefall, Paterson and Savage (1963) noted that *ice thicknesses* in the centre line were in the range 250 metres to 320 metres. Seismic studies, and drilling indicate over much of this area the bedrock surface beneath the glacier is at a level as much as 40 metres beneath the level of Sunwapta Lake.

Recent research programs by glaciologists Brugman and Demuth (1994), using radio echo sounding equipment, confirm the original depths obtained by Paterson and Savage (1963) using gravity and boreholes.

FLUCTUATIONS OF THE ICE FRONT

Evidence of Glacier Advance

Although the ice is continually moving down the valley, studies of the Athabasca Glacier indicate that the front of the glacier is in retreat. All of the pictures and historic documents available show us that in the recent past, the glacier was much larger. During an important period in time, the Little Ice Age, the glacier had advanced about 1.5 km beyond its present position. How do we know?

When a glacier invades a growing forest, the trees in its path are overridden and either damaged or killed, while trees only a few feet away are unscathed. When the ice thins and the terminus retreats, new trees will eventually grow in the formerly glaciated area. As a result, there is a distinct change from young vegetation on newly uncovered ground in comparison with mature vegetation in the area just beyond the outer limits of glaciation. The line separating these two types of vegetation is called the trimline. Glacial advances can be dated approximately by measuring the ages of trees on both sides of the trimline.

The trimline left by the Athabasca Glacier follows approximately the route of the former Banff-Jasper highway, from the Icefield Centre, for a distance of 0.9 km northwestward. From a study of growth rings of trees in the area, Field and Heusser (1954) believe the trimline was produced when the Athabasca Glacier advanced early in the 18th century.

Not all the facts are agreed upon about the extent of retreat by the Athabasca Glacier during the 18th century. This was a warmer, milder climatic period. According to Heusser (1956), the glacier had readvanced almost back to its maximum by the first half of the 19th century because of a global cooling trend.

The more recent great advance of the Athabasca Glacier was documented by noted geomorphologist Brian Luckman (1986). A short distance northwest of the Icefield Centre, he discovered a small moraine that was pushed into a grove of alpine firs. Luckman examined the cross-sections from one of the tilted and deformed trees, and he determined that the moraine pushed over the alpine firs in 1843-1844. Tree rings from a deformed tree provide the best estimate of the date of the maximum advance of the Athabasca Glacier during the Little Ice Age.

A Glacier in Retreat

A cumulative recession curve reveals intriguing aspects of the retreat of the Athabasca Glacier for the past 75 years. Beginning with the year 1922, the glacier had retreated about 265 metres from the estimated position in 1840. From the year 1922, to 1960 (38 years), the glacier retreated 1105 metres at an average rate of 29 metres per year. Between 1960 and 1980 (20 years), glacial recession slowed markedly and amounted to only 120 metres, at an average rate of 6 metres per year.

From the 1980's through 1992, the glacier responded to increased ablation and retreated about 111 metres, at an average rate of 9.2 metres per year. Measurements made between 1992 and 1994 show that the recession of the glacier has accelerated to over 24 metres per year.

Very high ablation rates during the two year period of 1992–1994 are spectacular, and the highest which I have recorded while exploring the Athabasca Glacier for over two decades. Short-term measurements show that the glacier terminus retreated 29 metres during a 5 month period in 1992 (May 1–October 1). Of course, this is somewhat misleading, since we know the glacier toe will advance approximately 7 metres during the following winter months, with little ablation taking place.

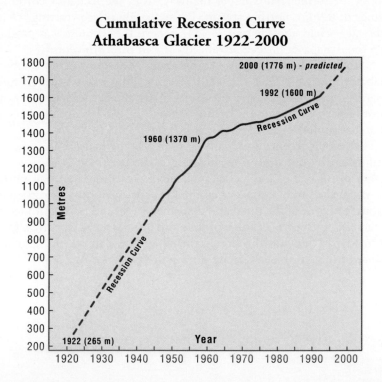

Cumulative Recession Curve
Athabasca Glacier 1922-2000

It is noteworthy that the high rate of retreat beginning in 1992 is somewhat comparable to the rate of recession between 1922 and 1960 when the Athabasca Glacier retreated 1100 metres at an average rate of 29 metres per year.

Although the glacier terminus is in retreat, measurements using time-lapse cinematography at the toe show that ice close to the bedrock contact is moving down-valley at 0.15 to 0.25 cm/hour: the faster rate occurring during warm afternoon hours. This is conclusive evidence that even when the position of the ice front is retreating, the glacier itself continues to move forward.

The Disappearing Glacier

On a hike along the terminus of the Athabasca Glacier, you will discover that the glacial front constantly experiences change, sometimes imperceptably, but on occasion with dramatic results. Significant changes are also taking place elsewhere on the glacier. From July 1–July 16, 1992, I measured the amount of downwasting taking place in the area of the glacier traversed by the Snocoaches.

If we compare the downwasting (melting and evaporation) of two areas on the glacier during the same period of time, some interesting differences are revealed. The ice surface at the Snocoach turnaround, at an elevation of 2200 metres, had an ablation rate of 3.0 cm/day, but at a lower elevation (2100 metres) the ice disappeared at a rate of 5.6 cm/day. Careful scientific readings show that the ablation rate and downwasting of the ice surface decreases at higher altitudes of the glacier.

Kite and Reid (1977), in an interesting article, calculated the change in volume of the Athabasca Glacier over the last 100 years. By retracing glacier surface contours as they would have appeared in relation to the lateral moraine in 1870, they show that the volume of the glacier ice in its ablation zone is only about two-thirds of its volume in 1870. Under present climatic conditions, this is an ominous situation for the Athabasca and its neighboring glaciers.

Retreat of Athabasca Glacier Since 1840

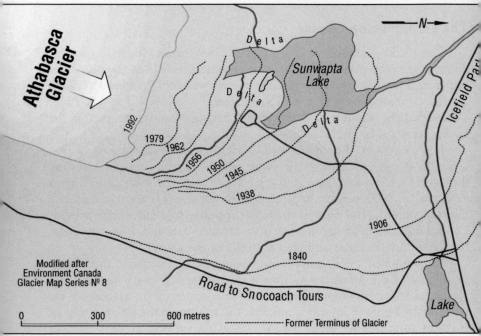

Athabasca Glacier

Delta

Delta

Delta

Sunwapta Lake

Icefield Park

1992
1979
1962
1956
1950
1945
1938
1906
1840

Road to Snocoach Tours

Lake

Modified after
Environment Canada
Glacier Map Series Nº 8

0   300   600 metres

------------- Former Terminus of Glacier

Trilobite (Alberta helena) of Middle Cambrian age (over 500 million years old) found in rocks of marine origin southeast of Athabasca Glacier (actual size 3 cm long). Other fossils from ancient seas are found in high ridges above the glacial valleys.

Growth of lichen on boulder in moraine near Sunwapta Lake. This moraine was deposited by the retreating Athabasca Glacier.

HOW DOES THE GLACIER ERODE BEDROCK?

Over wide areas just beyond the toe of the glacier, the bedrock has been abraded by glacier action. Long striations as well as grooves were caused by gravel and boulders being dragged along in the basal ice and rubbed across the bedrock under considerable ice pressure. The finest striations appear as a brilliant polish which can be seen when sunlight reflects off the surface. The presence of rock fragments in the basal ice is crucial, for clean ice will not abrade solid rock.

Along the south side of Sunwapta Lake, each rocky knoll has a smooth, curving slope facing up-glacier. However, there is a more jagged, steeper slope on the down-glacier or leeside of the knolls. The steep, craggy leeside of the knolls undergoes freezing and thawing, leading to rock fracturing. Angular rock fragments are literally plucked away by the action of the glacier as it moves down the valley.

As the Athabasca Glacier moves, it is eroding the bedrock beneath it. This powerful erosion will enlarge the future lake basin, 40 meters deeper than the present level of Sunwapta Lake. (profile on pages 38-39)

Striated and grooved bedrock surface near the base of Little Dome.

GLACIAL SCULPTURE

The Columbia Icefield is ringed by steep-sided outlet valleys, where glaciers have remodeled a far older terrain. The Athabasca Glacier did not create its valley, but has overwhelmed a former stream channel that was reshaped during an earlier period of glacial erosion. As the glacier continues to melt and retreat in the future, it will reveal a valley descending from the icefield in long bedrock steps. These resistant steps or cliffs are now hidden beneath the chaotic facade of the icefalls. Over thousands of years, the ice has deepened and widened the old stream valley into a classic U shape, known to offer the least resistance to the flowing ice.

Some snowfields and tributary glaciers are formed in natural mountain amphitheaters called *cirques*. Considered to be among the most interesting, and beautiful of all alpine erosional features, cirques are often known as the birthplace for many Rocky Mountain glaciers.

Falling snow is swept from high peaks into more protected places on lee slopes where it builds perennial snow banks. Eventually, these snowfields become more compact and turn into ice, which later begins to move in the form of tributary valley glaciers. Above the glaciers, the rock walls are highly shattered by frost action. Cirques are usually more awesome on north-facing slopes, where they are protected from direct exposure to the sun. Geologic structure also affects their size and orientation along the Continental Divide.

Sunwapta Lake basin also owes its origin to excavation by ice. There is a close relationship between the location of Sunwapta Lake and the type of bedrock, for the lake bed is at least 10 metres deep, in a zone of thin-bedded, easily eroded limestone rocks, softer than the surrounding bedrock. All of these features reveal the relentless power of a glacier dramatically altering ancient landscapes.

Glacial striations cutting across limestone outcrop near glacier terminus.

GLACIAL DEPOSITION

Lateral Moraines

Formidable peaks and cliffs rising above the Athabasca Glacier and the adjacent valley glaciers are composed mainly of limestone with some slate and quartzite. The rocks are highly susceptible to frost shattering, because they have many fractures in which water collects and freezes. Rock fragments break off, tumble down onto the ice, and accumulate between the valley wall and the ice surface. As a result, the sides of the glacier become lined with long ridges of debris of varying thickness (lateral moraines) carried by the ice. The ridge of debris is maintained even though the glacier moves out into a wider portion of the valley, and is not confined by valley walls. Lateral moraines along margins of the Dome and Athabasca Glaciers are exceptionally well defined.

A cover of fallen rock debris slows the melting of the underlying ice along the glacier margins. Thus, the more rapidly disappearing clean ice

Ground moraine deposited by the Athabasca Glacier was uncovered during the recent retreat of the ice. High lateral moraine is seen in middle ground.
Inset: Ptarmigan in summer plumage.

leaves the lateral moraine standing higher and higher in relation to the surface of the glacier. As melting progresses, the outer side of the moraine lies at stable, moderate angle, but the slope facing the glacier is much steeper, approaching 75° in places. The lateral moraine adjacent to the Snocoach loading zone has a slope of about 52° and is eroding about 30 cm/year, on average.

The height of the lateral moraines associated with glaciers gives some indication of the thickness of the ice during their formation. The moraine just cast of the terminus of the Athabasca Glacier maintains its knife-edged ridge and presently reaches a height of 124 metres above the valley floor. If we assume that the crest of the moraine at this location approximates the former height of the glacier during its maximum advance in the 1840's, then the ice has downwasted at rate of about one metre per year.

Longitudinal Profile

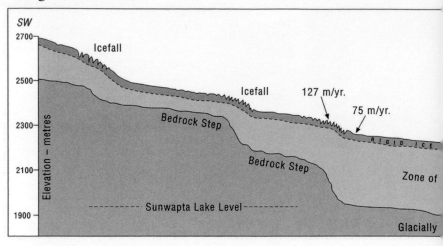

SW

Elevation – metres

2700 —

2500 —

2300 —

2100 —

1900 —

Icefall

Icefall

Bedrock Step

Bedrock Step

127 m/yr.

75 m/yr.

R I G I D   I C E

Zone of

- - - Sunwapta Lake Level - - -

Glacially

Looking down glacier toward Wilcox Ridge. Transverse crevasse in foreground.

ATHABASCA GLACIER

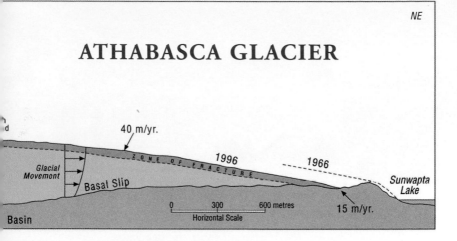

40 m/yr.

ZONE OF FRACTURE

1996

1966

Glacial Movement

Basal Slip

Sunwapta Lake

Basin

| 0 | 300 | 600 metres |

Horizontal Scale

15 m/yr.

Retreat of the ice front between 1960 and 1992 has exposed bedrock knolls extending across the valley.

Magnificent snow blankets the Athabasca Glacier and its moraines.

Ablation Moraines

The magnificent Dome, Stutfield, and Kitchener Glaciers exhibit surfaces almost entirely blanketed by rock rubble called ablation moraine. This relatively thin, yet insulating mantle of debris is derived from the steep lateral moraines and disintegrating mountain slopes above. It has a coarse texture, because the finer material has been washed out by meltwater. Explorations of the Dome Glacier reveal that the ablation moraine is commonly less than one metre thick, and the ice beneath the protective cover is exceptionally clean.

The dirty ice cliff which forms a small portion of the toe of Athabasca Glacier southwest of Sunwapta Lake is composed of ice covered by 1 to 2 metres of rock debris. A sequence of photographs taken from the same camera position each year for the last decade show that the cliff retreats approximately 6 metres each year, and at the same time the surface is downwasting about 2 metres per year. During warm, sunny days one can observe the action of melting ice and avalanching of rocks down the 25 metre high ice cliff. Scientists and Parks Canada interpreters studying the action at the ice cliff, or entering into an ice cave report close calls from falling boulders or collapsing ice cave ceilings. All of us have felt very fortunate to escape ourselves, with our camera equipment intact.

Ground Moraines

Below the ice mass, there is constant action at the base of the ice, usually hidden from view. Rock fragments are being deposited beneath the glacier and can accumulate on the striated and smoothed bedrock.

When the glaciers advanced, they deposited ground moraine which now can be seen in front of the Athabasca Glacier. Its low, undulating topography is broken by several morainal ridges east of Sunwapta Lake. The moraine is well exposed north of the lake, where it caps low bedrock ridges, and is approximately 4 metres thick.

Much of the ground moraine is deposited by pressure melting beneath the actively moving ice, allowing rock fragments to become freed and then lodged or plastered onto the glacier bed. This was captured on time-lapse films, showing that there was gradual release of rock fragments as the base of the glacier melted and moved down valley. Until these geological research films were made, it had never been recorded just how this process evolved, or how long it took to happen. Eight hours of glacial action under the ice is compressed in my films to 30 seconds on the screen.

The Dome Glacier is noted for its remarkable mantle of rock fragments, known as ablation moraine, insulating the glacier.

Annual Moraines

Glacial debris deposited in a 120 metre-wide zone between the delta parking area and the bedrock ridge in front of the glacier is not random, for it occurs as well-defined, but discontinuous ridges. These curved ridges are 0.7 to 2 metres high, and lie 2 to 20 metres apart, trending parallel to the glacier front. A series of still photographs, taken from the same camera position at the crest of the high lateral moraine east of the glacier, reveals some interesting facts about the origin of the debris ridges during the 1960's and 1970's.

During the summer months, the melting glacier retreats, depositing moraine composed of a mixture of clay, sand, pebbles and boulders. Some of the debris represents material which has been carried at the base of the glacier and plastered on bedrock by moving ice, while some has been carried to the toe of the glacier in shear zones. By mid-September of each melt season the glacier recedes as much as 20 metres, and no ridge of rock debris is left in front of the ice.

With the onset of winter, the rate of glacier movement exceeds the rate of melt, and the glacier advances over some of the moraine exposed during the previous summer. By the middle of May, the glacier has advanced as much as 10 metres from its previous position in September, and a sharp-crested ridge of debris is found at the terminus.

Evidence suggests that these low ridges of debris are *annual moraines* produced, not by pauses during general shrinkage of the Athabasca Glacier, but rather by an advance of ice pushing the snowbanks and debris during winter months. Measurements show that the moraines became closely spaced during the 1960's and 1970's. This coincides with the reduced rate of retreat of the Athabasca Glacier between 1960 and 1980.

Annual moraine of 1977 at the toe of the Athabasca Glacier; debris-laden ice at left.

Recessional moraines in front of Athabasca Glacier formed during temporary pauses of the recession of the glacier.

Recessional Moraines

When the Athabasca Glacier pauses in its retreat, ridges of rock debris are built up along the terminus of the ice. Some of this debris was carried along the base of the glacier and some of it was contained inside the ice as thin lenses of debris in shear planes. When a glacier front remains stationary, movement of the ice down-valley continues to feed the shear zone with rock fragments which are heaped in a moraine at the front of the glacier.

Well-defined recessional moraines were formed along the front of the Athabasca Glacier in approximately 1900, 1908, 1925 and 1935. The first date is based on studies of tree cores. The remainder are estimated from photographs in 1908 by Mary Schäffer, and in 1922 by Field, and from positions selected by the Dominion Water and Power Board of that era.

The unsorted rock debris in these moraines can be seen along the road on the way to the glacier terminus. Arcuate ridges 3 to 6 metres high by 200 metres long are composed of fragments ranging from blocks one metre long to clay-size particles. Late afternoon light accentuates the distinctive recessional moraines when viewed from Wilcox Pass.

The Dome Glacier also has recessional moraines, with the oldest (1846) located 0.65 km in front of the glacier. The rate of retreat of the Dome Glacier has been about 7 metres per year. The slow recession rate is attributed to insulation provided by the protective ablation moraine covering so much of the glacial surface.

Recessional moraines in the Athabasca and Dome glacier area provide us with keys to the nature and history of glacier recession in the Icefield region. Although the glaciers in the vicinity continue to recede, the Columbia Glacier (a magnificent outlet glacier) advanced dramatically as much as 1 km between 1966 and 1977 (Baranowski and Henoch, 1978).

Summary of Glaciers in the Columbia Icefield Area

Glacier	Area km2	Length km	Elev. of Head m.	Elev. of Terminus m.	Length at Max Advance (Post 1800) km.	Elev. of Toe at Max. Advance m.
Athabasca	6.34	6.0	2700	2000	7.50	1900
Dome	5.92	5.7	3200	1980	6.60	1900
Stutfield	5.68	5.2	2740	1770	6.00	1680
Kitchener	2.17	2.8	3020	2070	3.65	1980
Little Athabasca	2.03	2.4	3290	2290	3.55	2040
Sunwapta	0.97	2.3	3140	2300	3.10	2160
Athabasca Tributary (East)	0.75	1.7	2940	2350	2.25	2160
Athabasca Tributary (West)	0.50	1.3	3050	2380	1.45	2290
Stutfield Tributary	0.43	1.0	2320	2090	1.50	1920
Kitchener Tributary	0.39	1.2	2860	2510	1.70	2380
Little Dome	0.16	0.6	2590	2440	0.85	2410
Nigel Peak	0.15	0.8	2700	2470	1.15	2440

From Kucera and Henoch (1978)

GLACIAL MELTWATER

Meltwater Channels and Moulins

Small pools and rivulets form on the surface of the Athabasca Glacier during early spring. As days begin to lengthen, with temperatures on the rise, stream channels become wider and deeper and carry greater volumes of meltwater. By August, some rushing streams have carved steep channels over a metre wide on the ice surface. The stream patterns reveal that the centre axis of the glacier is higher than the lateral margins of the ice, for most of the streams eventually flow toward the edges of the glacier.

As you would expect, meltwater streams are affected by daily temperatures, for there is a lower rate of stream volume in the early morning, then rising rapidly in the late afternoon. Streams often meander in their channels for long distances over the surface of the glacier before vanishing into openings in the ice.

As meltwater plunges into openings, the swirling motion rounds them into deep holes in the ice known as moulins. In one summer during the 1990's, I mapped the location of 146 moulins on the glacier.

Caution is advised near moulins, for these deep holes present danger to anyone traversing the glacier. The rounded vertical walls, the cascading water, and great depth of the moulins make rescue attempts difficult. Moulins are usually deeper and more treacherous than crevasses. The water flows violently in chutes, usually reaching the base of the ice mass, where it forms subglacial streams.

Beneath the glacial surface, tunnels carry the meltwater within and beneath the ice, and become interconnected at different levels of the glacier. A change in position of the subglacial or internal plumbing system of the Athabasca Glacier can result in abrupt changes in the location and volume of the meltwater streams emerging from the base of the glacier.

Meltwater derived from the tributary glacier on the east side of the Athabasca Glacier flows directly down steep, rocky ledges and plunges into a large moulin on the east flank of the Athabasca Glacier, about 610 metres south of the Snocoach loading area. It penetrates at least 30 metres below the glacier surface, and then becomes a powerful stream emerging from a tunnel at the northeast edge of the glacier terminus. The torrent of water rushing through this tunnel may at times account for seventy percent of the meltwater emerging from the snout of the glacier. The Parks Canada interpretive staff have information regarding streams, moulins, and crevasses. *They should be consulted regarding any glacial traverse.*

Meandering meltwater channel on the Athabasca Glacier.

Glacial meltwater plunges into a very large and deep moulin, eventually to reach the terminus of the glacier.

Ablation moraine approximately 300 metres in front of Dome Glacier.

Limestone boulders create a meltwater cascade, descending from the glacier on Mt. Athabasca.

SUNWAPTA LAKE AND DELTAS

Sunwapta Lake appeared only a moment ago in geologic time. The brief life of this glacially scoured lake began in the late 1930's. Until then, remarkable photographs and fine sketches made by early explorers show a deep and wide expanse of glacial ice covering a great area of the valley, but there was no lake to be seen.

The Athabasca Glacier has retreated for over 150 years, and in 1938 it exposed the northern edge of a rock basin. The abrasive debris carried in the base of the glacier had carved this depression when the glacier advanced during the Little Ice Age. The lake, which gives rise to the Sunwapta River, grew larger over later decades until reaching its greatest extent in 1966. By the 1990's, however, the lake was only 500 metres long and 350 metres wide.

Aerial photographs, as well as images taken from high ridges continue to record how the lake is evolving. Time-lapse cinematography is perhaps the best way to show that the meltwater streams flowing from the glacier to the lake shift their channels constantly in the warm days of spring and summer. As the channels shifted, the load of rock debris was deposited over a broad area, forming a large delta, which has grown extensively since 1956. Within the next few years the delta will grow shore to shore.

By comparing the size and shape of the delta on 1965 and 1979 aerial photographs we can determine that the delta advanced 40 metres into Sunwapta Lake during a 14 year period, a rate of about 2.8 metres per year. Recent geological studies indicate that the migration of the delta accelerated to about 6.1 metres per year, advancing 80 metres farther into the lake between 1979 and 1992. The movement of sand, silt and cobbles has engulfed former bedrock islands in the lake

Another stream enters Sunwapta Lake on the east, but its source is melting snow and ice on Mt. Athabasca. It has formed a fan-delta that has advanced only 9.5 metres between 1979 and 1992.

The volume of glacial debris entering the lake is awesome. In a scientific study, Mathews (1964) calculated the volume of sediment transported into Sunwapta Lake during 1957. For one 24 hour period, an estimated 380 metric tons of silt and clay and 190 tons of sand were brought into Sunwapta Lake by two glacial streams. Out of this amount, only four to seven tons of silt and clay left the lake by way of the Sunwapta River. Gilbert and Shaw (1981) estimated that the lake trapped 78% of the sediment that flowed into it each year.

Sunwapta Lake will have a limited history, engulfed in the future by its deltas. Only a significant reversal in climate could prolong the life of the lake, which was larger, and long ago in the 1960's exhibited beautiful small icebergs floating on its surface.

A delta is invading Sunwapta Lake at the rate of about 6.1 metres/year.

THE SUNWAPTA FLOODS

Stream flow gauges monitor the Sunwapta River as it surges from Sunwapta Lake. Records of summer discharge have been kept by Canadian Government hydrologists since 1948. In 1964, a University of B.C. geologist, W.H. Mathews, correlated mean daily discharge of the Sunwapta River with air temperatures at Jasper, 92 km northwest of the Icefield Centre. In the study, daily stream flow was related primarily to the temperatures of the current day. Mathews also noted a significant day to night fluctuation in meltwater from the Athabasca Glacier into the lake.

An intriguing feature of the stream flow record for the Athabasca Glacier was the occurrence of "jokulhlaups", an Icelandic term for very high discharge initiated from within a glacier. These floods interrupted the normal day to night cycle, and were unrelated to the weather. Records covering 13 summers showed at least 10 floods having discharges of 250,000 m³ or more, and one flood released 1,400,000 m³ of water. Because there are no ice-dammed lakes around the Athabasca Glacier, it is believed that the water was stored within the ice! Drainage of a single ice chamber during the large flood would have caused some subsidence of the glacier surface, but this was not observed. The water must have been contained in numerous cavities. Strange cavities in the glacial ice were noticed by Savage and Paterson during their drilling program in 1962.

Compare the position of the glacier toe and configuration of the delta on 1992 (above) and 1979 aerial photos. In 13 years, the terminus of the glacier retreated over 100 metres, and the delta advanced 80 metres into Sunwapta Lake.

GLACIAL OUTWASH

When glaciers advance, they have the power to carry a debris load within the ice, as well as at the base of the glacier. Meltwater streams flowing from the margin of the ice sort the debris, and then deposit it as glacial outwash. For example, across a distance of 0.5 km from the terminus of the Dome glacier, the outwash contains numerous boulders two metres long. Outwash in the Sunwapta Valley is composed of rounded gravels and cobbles deposited during recession of the Dome and Athabasca Glaciers since the 1840's. The floor of the valley is 0.3 to 0.5 km wide, and coarse gravels extend 4 km down-valley to the Sunwapta River canyon. The deposits left by the meltwater are very well stratified, unlike the more chaotic, unsorted glacial till in the lateral moraines.

Because of a large debris load, the Sunwapta River has multiple braided channels continually changing course. This is an instance where time-lapse cinematography accurately records the geologic activity from a vantage point near the entrance of Sunwapta Canyon. During a 72 hour period in August, 1974, a 1.0 km stretch of Sunwapta River was shown on film, as it rapidly shifted its channels and miniature terraces. The floor of the valley has little or no vegetation over most of its width, because of the unstable and variable nature of the river.

Outwash composed of gravel and cobbles mantles the floor of Sunwapta Valley. The river flows in a constantly changing, braided pattern.

TRIBUTARY GLACIER

TRIBUTARY GLACIER

AVALANCH SLOPE

LARGE MOULIN

PRESENT SNOCOACH DEPARTURE

FORMER SNOCOACH DEPARTURE

MARGINAL CREVASSE

SNOCOACH RD.

CAUSEWAY

OLD ACCESS ROAD

12 M/YR

LATERAL MORAINE

ROCK DEBRIS ON ICE

15 M

MELTWATER TUNNEL

1979 TE

1966 TERMINUS

TRAIL

1956 TERMINUS

STREAM FROM MT. ATHABASCA

1945 TERMINUS

UMBIA ICEFIELD

BEDROCK OF
CAMBRIAN AGE

ICEFALLS

TRANSVERSE CREVASSES

127 M/YR

75 M/YR.

AVALANCHE
FAN

MEDIAL MORAINE

40 M/YR.

ROCK DEBRIS ON ICE

1964

LATERAL MORAINE

MELTWATER
TUNNEL

BEDROCK

DELTA

Sunwapta Lake

DELTA

ATHABASCA GLACIER 1992
View from Wilcox Ridge

RECENT OBSERVATIONS

Glacial Transport

Aerial photographs provide geologists with excellent ways to interpret long-term glacial history, and to record brief historic milestones as well. From the aerial view, a remnant of the old access road that led from the moraine onto the glacier 1977 through 1979 can still be seen as an island of rock debris on the natural ice surface. This oval mass measures 102 metres long and 60 metres wide, and rests on the east edge of the glacier. The air photo is included in this edition (pages 58 and 59).

To demonstrate the force of glacial transport, it is possible to see on the photo, the section of the old road that was carried down the valley for a distance of 220 metres (by 1992) at an average rate of 17 metres per year. Based on the average rates of retreat, as well as glacial velocity during the 1979–1992 period, the leading edge of this football field-sized road remnant may reach the terminus of the glacier by the year 2011.

Moderating Effects of Snow

We have discovered that the natural ablation of the glacier in successive seasons eventually eliminates many traces of travel on the ice surface. It has been shown that the route of the Snocoach roadway on the glacier surface during 1989–1992 was considerably modified by ablation taking place on the Athabasca Glacier by September, 1993.

Athabasca Glacier cradled between magnificent escarpments shows renowned tour route taken by Snocoaches. Inset: Front of an avalanche.

Snow accumulates to a greater thickness in low areas on the glacier, including on the former ice roads. Snow serves to protect the route from excessive melting early in the ablation season, while there is concurrent melting of adjacent glacier ice. With a protective layer of reflective white snow, topographic relief between the roadway and the glacier lessens through successive seasons.

To take advantage of the insulating benefits of the crucial blanket of snow, Brewster Transportation and Tours now uses the same Snocoach road for only two consecutive seasons, lessening the impact on the glacier surface. By moving the route across the glacier periodically, natural conditions can prevail over the years.

MOUNTAIN SLOPES THAT MOVE

From 1959–1995, geological studies made on the glacier, and on aerial photographs, showed many dynamic physical changes which had taken place on the slopes adjacent to the Athabasca Glacier.

In 1959, the high lateral moraine on the east side of the glacier was slightly broken at the crest, and descended gradually from the old visitor parking lot for a distance of 1.3 kilometres to the north. However, by 1964 (after construction of the access road and parking lot in 1961), the moraine clearly began to show more fracturing.

Slope instability caused the closure of the old access road, parking area, and old snowmobile complex in 1983. The new Snocoach loading area was then constructed 200 metres north of the former one. The new location occupies an area cut into a rock glacier, as well as the east slope of the lateral moraine.

In 1994, engineering survey stations were placed in the vicinity of the Snocoach loading area. Measurements made during 1994 and 1995 indicated that the mountain slope, lateral moraine, and Snocoach loading complex are being displaced downward and westward toward the Athabasca Glacier. The moraine in the vicinity of the Snocoach loading area was slowly collapsing along several fractures, and the entire rubble-covered mountain slope to the east had slipped as much as 68 metres toward the Athabasca Glacier (by 1996). It has also been displaced downward approximately 44 metres.

Our measurements in 1995 indicated that the area was being displaced at the rate of 1.8 metres/year, an increase from an average velocity of 1.27 metres/year during the 1959–1992 period. Measurements also reveal that both vertical and lateral movements increase rapidly between May and October, but decrease dramatically during winter months.

Historic aerial photograph taken August 7, 1961 (University of Washington). The moraine has a sharp unbroken crest for its entire length. During this time the glacier was bordered by Sunwapta Lake.

Cause of Accelerated Slope Movements

Glaciological reports from such distant mountain ranges in Switzerland, Argentina, and Alaska have confirmed that downwasting of valley glaciers contributes to accelerated slope movement on adjacent mountainsides. Downwasting of the ice surface increases the relief (vertical differences in height) between the moraine and the surface of the glacier with time. The same conditions may be seen on the slopes above the Athabasca Glacier.

Slope movement increases during the ablation season, suggesting a distinct relationship with lowering of the ice surface. To study the rate of ablation, a glaciological monitoring station on the glacier west of the access road records a lowering of the ice surface. Glaciologist Mindy Brugman measured downwasting due to ablation of the glacier in 1994 and 1995, on behalf of the National Hydrology Research Centre. The station recorded that the ice surface was lowered about 5.5 metres at the rate of 5.8 cm/day, from June 28 to October 1, 1994.

My geological studies during the 1990's recorded that the collapse of the lateral moraine and movement of the rock rubble slopes in the vicinity of the Snocoach loading area coincides with the *natural lowering* of the ice surface from June through October. Rapid downwasting of the glacier tends to increase the vertical relief of the lateral moraine, and at the same time removes the lateral support, thus decreasing the shearing resistance of the mountain slope above, and promoting slippage. As temperatures cool in the late fall and winter, slope movements decrease. Instability of slopes is a long-term geological engineering factor in this glaciated valley, and careful monitoring of slope movement will continue to be vital in the Columbia Icefield region.

Road to the Snocoach complex, through the high lateral moraine.

Aerial photograph (1992) of the lower portion of the Athabasca Glacier showing the dynamic geology of the area. The glacier has lost about one-third of its volume of ice, accelerating the rate of slope movement.

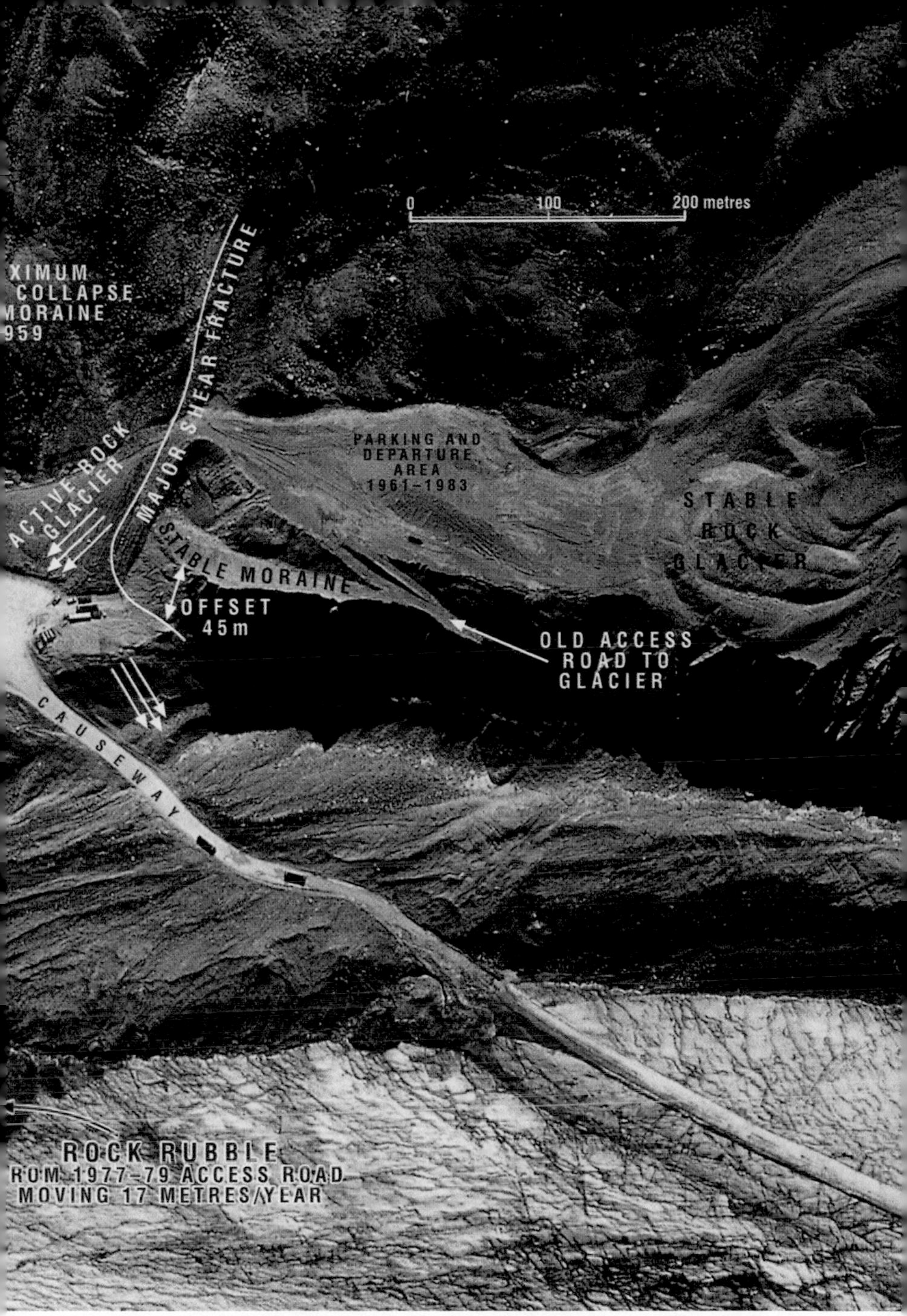

0 100 200 metres
XIMUM
COLLAPSE
MORAINE
959
MAJOR SHEAR FRACTURE
ACTIVE ROCK GLACIER
PARKING AND DEPARTURE AREA 1961–1983
STABLE ROCK GLACIER
STABLE MORAINE
OFFSET 45m
OLD ACCESS ROAD TO GLACIER
CAUSEWAY
ROCK RUBBLE
ROM 1977–79 ACCESS ROAD
MOVING 17 METRES/YEAR

MOUNTAIN SLOPES ON THE MOVE

AVALANCHE ACTIVITY

Precipitous slopes and extreme temperature fluctuations are among the factors leading to frequent avalanche activity at the head of the glacial valleys surrounding the Columbia Icefield. In this unstable environment, snowfall is heavy and the terrain nearly vertical, with overhanging ice cliffs. At altitudes of 2500 to 2700 metres, severe changes in temperature and moisture content cause instability of the snowpack. Storms sweep in from British Columbia, greatly worsening the avalanche danger by increasing the weight of the snow. High winds have a potentially deadly effect as well.

There is a more important, and different physical process taking place at the edge of the Columbia Icefield. Here, the tremendous outward pressure of ice which caps the steep escarpments bordering the icefield gives rise to a periodic collapse of ice on its outer margin. This results in the ominous sounds often mistaken for thunder across the valley, as the broken ice falls from the high ramparts of the icefield.

Hiking on the glacier on warm summer days, I have witnessed avalanches taking place on high southeast-facing cliffs above the Athabasca Glacier. Along with film crews, we have experienced some near-misses, as blocks of snow and ice fell hundreds of metres, after plunging down from

Intermittent collapse of ice caves at the terminus of the glacier on Mount Andromeda have formed avalanche cones in the vicinity of the Snocoach turnaround.

the bedrock cliffs. Huge ice blocks (some larger than a car) have crashed on the upper part of an ice fan, and careened further down the slope on a destructive journey. Similar events have taken place over the centuries, resulting in this impressive avalanche fan built up on the northwest side of the Athabasca Glacier.

Devastating ice avalanches can can also originate from the collapse of ice caves at the terminus of the tributary glacier emerging from Mt. Andromeda. *Extreme caution is advised in this dangerous area.*

A GLIMPSE INTO THE PAST

In 1986 and 1988, Dr. Brian Luckman conducted extensive scientific studies to determine the age of the glacier and its moraines. He collected wood fragments from the toe of the Athabasca Glacier which yielded radiocarbon dates ranging from 7550 ±100 to 8230 ±80 years. These ancient tree fragments indicated that several thousand years ago, mature pine and fir trees were growing on the valley floor some distance up-valley from the present terminus of the Athabasca Glacier. This is significant paleobotanical evidence strongly indicating that conditions were generally warm and mild during that period, and that the entire ice mass of the glacier was far less extensive than it is today.

Banded limestone boulder left in the wake of retreat of the Athabasca Glacier 50 years ago. The field of boulders resembles a landscape from Mars.

A LOOK INTO THE FUTURE

How can we predict the fate of glaciers and icefields which provide much of the beauty of the Rocky Mountains? In the elusive span of geologic time, we can look for evidence which might reveal the course of future events.

In the last 150 years, although the Athabasca Glacier continuously flowed slowly down its valley, the terminus of the glacier has retreated dramatically. During the same period, the glacier has lost over 30% of its volume of ice. The rate of glacial retreat in the early 1990's has accelerated to a rate that is four times greater than the recession which we observed during our initial glacial research projects of the 1960's.

By reviewing the recent past, we discovered that if global warming continues, the glacier front will recede at this rapid rate, even though the main body of ice moves down-valley with velocities that have been somewhat consistent during the last 45 years. The glacier terminus could recede about 2.5 kilometres in approximately 100 to 150 years. The terminus will then exist very near the lower icefall. As the ice disappears, a glacially sculptured lake, would slowly appear in a bedrock basin formerly covered by the glacier. The retreating glacier will leave the lake as one of its major legacies in the geological setting of the future. As we have shown in the aerial photographs in the book, geologic activity is having a forceful effect on the survival of the surrounding mountain slopes, as well as the high, knife-edged moraine. Such slope instability is typical of moraines, throughout the mountains of the world.

The passage of time should cause changes on the Columbia Icefield at a much slower pace, for the vast area and depth of the huge mass of glacial ice will withstand destructive aspects of a warmer climate. If the icefield can resist increasingly warm rains, as well as a higher degree of solar radiation, its *unsurpassed glacial landscape* should remain far beyond our present generation.

After the long, overwhelming periods of world-wide glaciation which our planet has repeatedly experienced, our present interglacial period began about 10,000 years ago, and usually prevailed,(except for the return of the Little Ice Age).

Nature is delicately balanced throughout the bordering region of the Columbia Icefield. The Athabasca Glacier is vulnerable to sudden geologic and climatic events. The glacier may be affected by glacial outburst floods, collapsing valley walls, as well as many other dynamic erosional forces. If you look for the key to the future, study the rates of snow accumulation versus the rate of ablation (loss of ice). *It is evident that a steady supply of snow could extend the life of this spectacular glacier!*

Fortunately, a better future may await the stark landscape of recent moraines. As the climate moderates, masses of brilliant alpine flowers and spreading mats of mountain vegetation will undergo the natural progression of life, reclaiming the barren, rocky debris. Snowline should rise, and with it the forest, subalpine and alpine zones, where the wildlife will steadily return to higher terrain. After many decades, new featues appear in front of the Athabasca Glacier, and a greater array of plants and animals will slowly regain the land.

Future events are beyond our immediate vision, but change will not diminish the magnificent character of the Columbia Icefield. The story will be told in exhibits and films in the Glacier Gallery at the Icefield Centre, a heritage from our generation to the next.

It should be remembered, that with little warning the earth could return to another glacial epoch. What a different future this would imply! Time, and good research may allow us to predict this alternative kind of future, characterized by advancing glaciers throughout the Rocky Mountains.

The older moraine deposits in front of the Athabasca Glacier are first to be colonized.

ACKNOWLEDGEMENTS

For over two decades, many individuals from Parks Canada, Jasper National Park, made generous contributions of time and effort during my field research and film-making on the Athabasca Glacier.

Special appreciation is accorded to Mr. Jim Todgham, Parks Canada, Manager, Icefield Area Operations, for his enthusiastic interest and encouragement for geological studies at the Columbia Icefield. It is Mr. Todgham who had the vision to oversee the exceptional design and splendid completion of the exhibits in the Icefield Centre's Glacier Gallery which opened to great acclaim in 1996.

Outstanding cooperation with many aspects of major scientific engineering projects conducted in recent years at the Columbia Icefield was provided by Mr. Andrew Whittick, General Manager, Brewster Transportation and Tours Ltd., and his staff. Mr. Paul Wenger, also of the Brewster organization at the Columbia Icefield, provided valuable time for the placement of scientific equipment on the ice, and he shared his detailed knowledge of the early years of snowmobile history and Snocoach travel on the glacier.

This book is dedicated to my wife Pam, who contributed to the design and art direction of all my books, and to my son Steve, for his assistance conducting field studies on the glacier, as well as computing a number of publications related to the geology of this beautiful region.

Survival is difficult for alpine plants on windswept recent moraine.

SELECTED REFERENCES

Baranowski, S., and Henoch, W.E.S. and Kucera, R.E., (1978) *Glacier and Landform Features in the Columbia Icefield Area, Banff and Jasper National Parks, Alberta, Canada.* Glaciology Div., Inland Waters Directorate, Environment Canada, 158 p.

Brugman, M. and Demuth, M., 1994, *Structure and Basal Topography of the Athabasca Glacier: A Glaciological Interpretation and Recommendation for the Location of Near-ice Interpretive Facilities.* National Hydrology Research Institute Contracted Report March, 1994, Jasper National Park. 190 p.

Field, W.O., and Heusser, C.J., (1954) *Glacier and Botanical Studies in the Canadian Rockies,* 1953: Canadian Alpine Journal, v. 37, p. 128–140.

Gilbert, R.W. and Shaw, J., 1981, *Sedimentation in Proglacial Sunwapta Lake, Alberta.* Canadian Journal of Earth Sciences 18, p. 81–93.

Heusser, C.J., (1956) *Post-glacial Environments in the Canadian Rocky Mountains:* Ecological Monographs, v. 26, p. 263–302.

Kanasewich, E.R., (1963) *Gravity Measurements on the Athabasca Glacier, Alberta, Canada:* Jour. of Glaciol. v. 4, p. 617–631.

Kite, G .W., and Reid, I.A., (1977) *Volumetric Change of the Athabasca Glacier Over the Last 100 years.* Jour. of Hydrology. v. 32, p. 279–294.

Kucera, R.E., (1972) *Probing the Athabasca Glacier,* Evergreen Press, Vancouver, B.C., 32 p.

Kucera, R.E., (1972) *Time-Lapse Cinematography Applied to the Study of Geologic Processes at the Athabasca Glacier, Alberta, Canada.* Geol. Soc. Amer. Abst., v.4, No.3, p. 186–87.

Kucera, R.E., (1973) *Glacier on the Move:* 16 mm film, sound and colour. Distributed by Encyclopaedia Britannica Films, Hollywood Calif. and Toronto, Ontario.

Kucera, R.E., and Henoch, W.E.S., (1978) *Glacier and Landform Features in the Columbia Icefield Area, Banff and Jasper National Parks, Alberta, Canada.* Glaciology Div., Inland Waters Directorate, Environment Canada.

Kucera, R.E., 1978–1993, *Exploring the Columbia Icefield.* (four editions) High Country Colour, Calgary, Alberta.

Kucera, R.E., 1993–1996, Series of Geological Reports re: ablation and velocity studies of the Athabasca Glacier; and slope movements taking place in the Columbia Icefield area, Jasper National Park.

Luckman, B.H., 1986, *Landform Development in the Forefields of the Athabasca and Dome Glaciers.* Report to Parks Canada. December, 1986.

Mathews, W.H., (1964) *Sediment Transport from Athabasca Glacier, Alberta.* Publ. No. 65 of the I.A.S.H., General Assembly of Berkeley, Land Erosion, Precipitation, Hydrometry, Soil Moisture p. 155–165.

May, R.D., (1964) *Survey of Glaciers on Eastern Slope of Rocky Mountains in Banff and Jasper National Parks,* Dept. of Northern Affairs and National Resources, Water Resources Branch.

Neave, K.G., and Savage, J.C., (1970) *Icequakes on the Athabasca Glacier.* Journal of Geophysical Research, v. 75, No. 8, p. 1351–1362.

Paterson, W.S.B., (1969) *The Physics of Glaciers,* Pergamon Press, 250 p.

Paterson, W.S.B., and Savage J.C., (1963) *Geometry and Movement of the Athabasca Glacier:* Journal of Geophysical Research, v. 68, p. 4513–4520.

Paterson, W.S.B., (1971) *Temperature Measurements in Athabasca Glacier, Alberta, Canada.* Journal of Glaciology, v. 10, No. 60.

Raymond, C.F., (1971) *Flow in a Transverse Section of Athabasca Glacier, Alberta, Canada.* Jour. of Glaciol. v. 10, No. 55, p. 55–84.

Reid, I.A., and Charbonneau, J.O.G., (1964 and 1979) *Glacial Surveys in Alberta.* Water Resources Branch, Dept. of the Environment, Ottawa, Ontario.

Savage, J.C., and Paterson, W.S.B., (1963) *Borehole Measurements in the Athabasca Glacier:* Journal of Geophysical Research, v. 68, p. 4521-4536.

Sharp, R.P., (1960) *Glaciers.* Condon Lectures, Oregon State System of Higher Education, Oregon, 78p.

Stutfield, H.E.M. and Collie, J.N., (1903) *Climbs and Explorations in the Canadian Rockies;* London, Longmans, Green and Co., London, N.Y., 343p.

Striated boulder found in moraine near Icefield Centre. Alpine vegetation is reclaiming the once barren moraine.

GLOSSARY

Ablation – The wastage of snow and ice, by melting and evaporation.

Ablation area – That area of a glacier where loss of ice exceeds accumulation over the year.

Accumulation area – The area of the glacier where more snow accumulates than melts away during the year.

Braided stream – A stream with a myriad of channels which constantly interweave and change positions, creating unstable small terraces.

Cirque – Natural amphitheatre or basin carved by glacial erosion.

Crevasse – A fracture or fissure in the crust of the glacier, rarely exceeding 36 metres in depth. A result of stretching and breaking of brittle ice.

Dirt cone – A thin veneer of debris draping a cone of ice up to several metres high, formed because the debris has insulated the ice beneath it.

Firn – Granulated old snow in the transition phase between snow and ice. Formed in the accumulation zone of a glacier or icefield.

Foliation – Closely spaced layers of coarse bubbly, coarse clear, and fine-grained bluish ice, created by deformation at depth in the glacier.

Icefall – Heavily crevassed section of a glacier flowing over steep bedrock cliffs.

Icefield – An immense individual mass of ice which flows outward from its accumulation area. It replenishes valley outlet glaciers.

Little Ice Age – The period of time that led to expansion of valley and cirque glaciers world-wide, with their maximum extents being attained between 1700–1850 AD. (possibly 1840 for the Athabasca Glacier).

Moraine – Ridges or mounds of unsorted rock debris deposited by a glacier. There are many types of moraine covered in this book. They include lateral, ground, ablation, annual, and reccessional moraines.

Moulin – A water-carved opening in the glacial surface where meltwater exploits a weakness in the ice. Many moulins are cylindrical, up to several metres across, and may extend down to the glacier bed. Also known as glacier millwells.

Rock glacier – Very slow moving lobate mass of coarse, angular rock debris extending from the front of cliffs in a mountainous area.

Terminus – The lowest end of a glacier, also known as a glacier toe, or snout.

Till – Accumulation of unsorted mixtures of clay, silt, sand, gravel, and boulders. It is the usual composition of a moraine.

Tongue – Main body of an outlet glacier, flowing down an alpine valley.

Warm glacier – A glacier whose temperature is at the pressure melting point throughout, except for a cold layer of limited depth occurring in winter.

*Athabasca Glacier in the distance, with Mt. Athabasca in full sunlight.
Inset: Mountain sheep in high alpine meadow.*

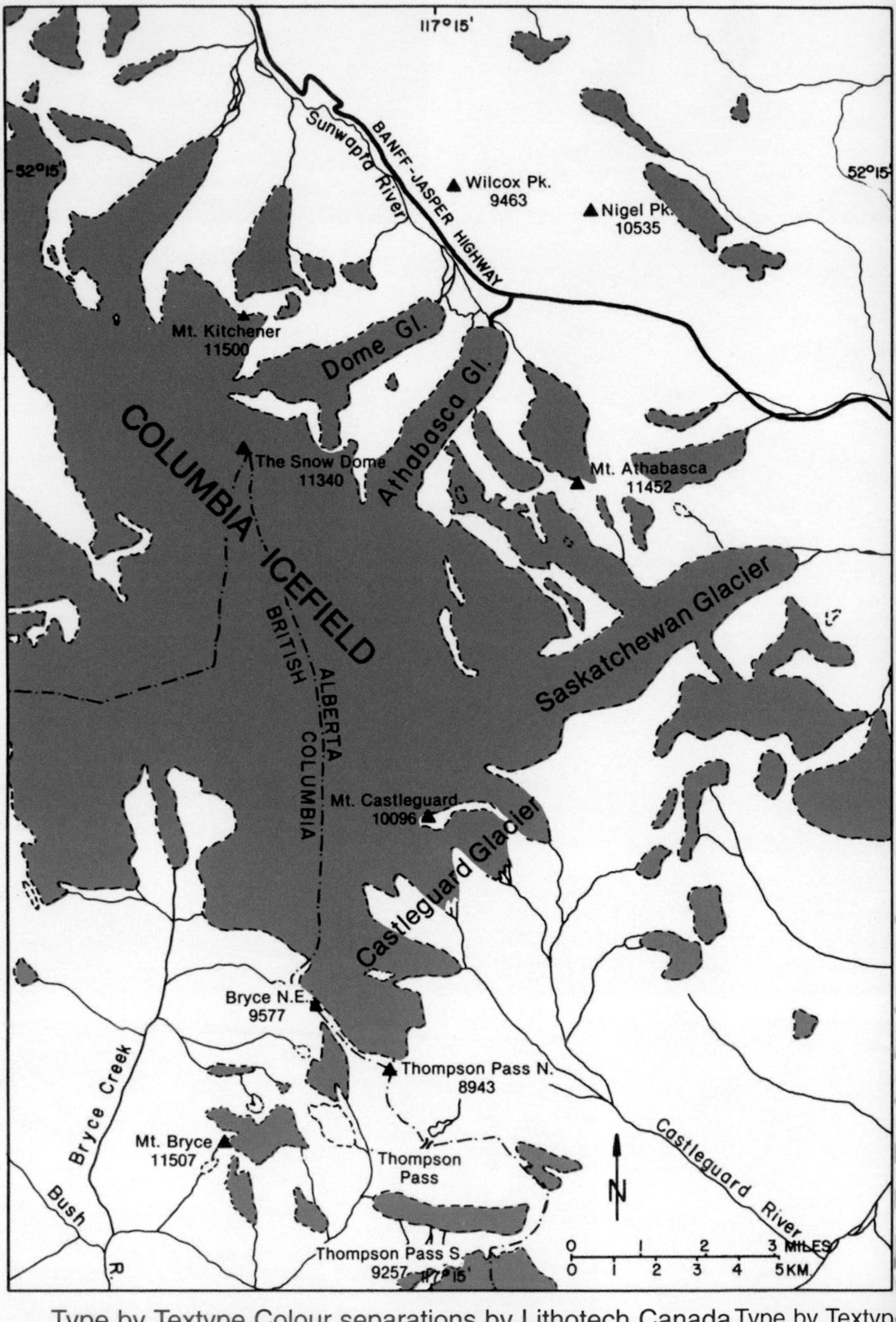
117°15'
52°15'
52°15'
Sunwapta River
BANFF-JASPER HIGHWAY
Wilcox Pk.
9463
Nigel Pk.
10535
Mt. Kitchener
11500
Dome Gl.
Athabasca Gl.
COLUMBIA ICEFIELD
The Snow Dome
11340
Mt. Athabasca
11452
Saskatchewan Glacier
BRITISH
ALBERTA
COLUMBIA
Mt. Castleguard
10096
Castleguard Glacier
Bryce N.E.
9577
Thompson Pass N.
8943
Bryce Creek
Mt. Bryce
11507
Thompson Pass
Castleguard River
Bush R.
Thompson Pass S.
9257
117°15'
N
0 1 2 3 MILES
0 1 2 3 4 5 KM

Type by Textype Colour separations by Lithotech Canada
Printed in Canada
Type by Textyp
Colour separations by Lithotech Canad

Printed in Canad